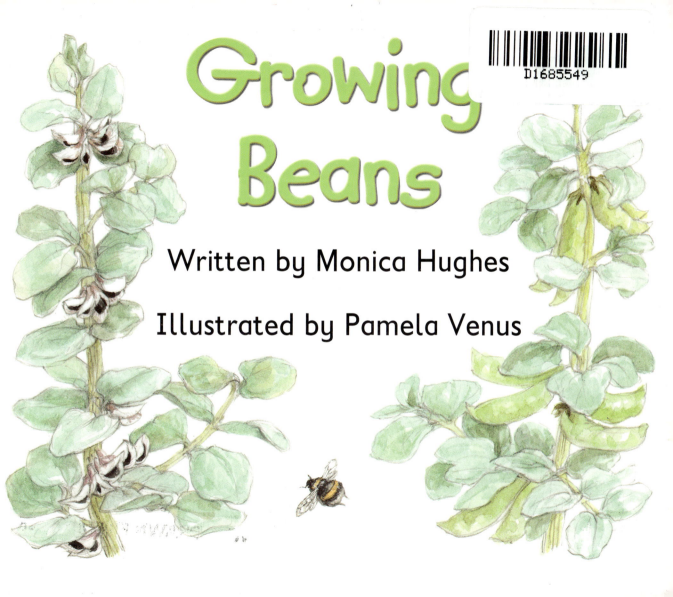

Growing Beans

Written by Monica Hughes

Illustrated by Pamela Venus

This is the way we dig the soil,

dig the soil, dig the soil.

This is the way we dig the soil,

in our little garden.

3

This is the way we weed the soil,

weed the soil, weed the soil.

This is the way we weed the soil,

in our little garden.

5

This is the way we plant the seeds,
plant the seeds, plant the seeds.
This is the way we plant the seeds,
in our little garden.

7

This is the way we water the shoots,

water the shoots, water the shoots.

This is the way we water the shoots,

in our little garden.

8

9

This is the way we pick the beans,

pick the beans, pick the beans.

This is the way we pick the beans,

in our little garden.

10

11

This is the way we eat the beans,

eat the beans, eat the beans.

This is the way we eat the beans,

in our little garden.

12

13

This is the way we grow the beans,
grow the beans, grow the beans.
This is the way we grow the beans,
in our little garden.

3

4

5

6

15

Lifecycle of a bean

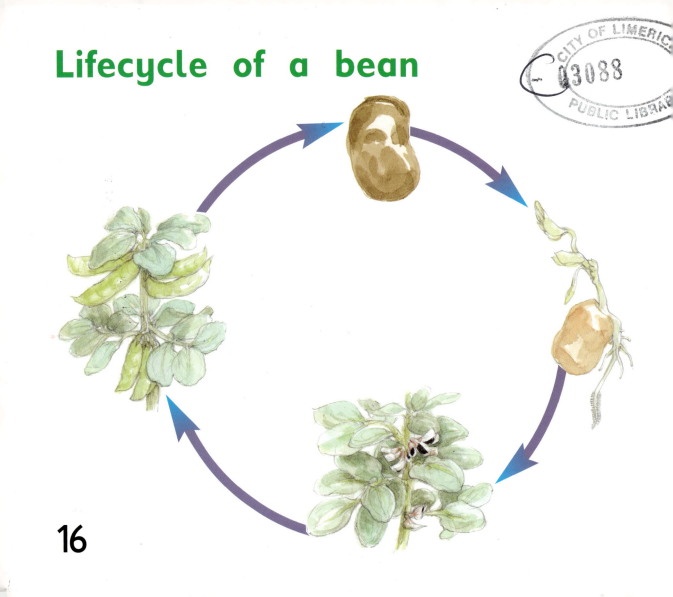

16